# PLANNING YOUR DAY

# -101-

## Weekend & Summer Edition

### Sara Williams

This book is dedicated to **Sabrina Williams**, my wife and driving force, whose support makes dreams possible.

# ACKNOWLEDGMENTS

Thank you to the individuals who contributed
to the publication of this book:

## Hillary Melchiors
a creative mind, a mother to emulate,
and a soul that smiles

## Sarah Elaman
a caring mother and counselor, and a friend

## Michael Shockley
a loving father, a skilled editor, and a friend

## Susan Kumleben
a parent coach and a new long-distance friend,
whose words inspire from across the pond

## Kelly Howard Engelbrecht
my mother and my encouragement,
a teacher always and a friend forever

# A LETTER TO THE ADULTS

You are preparing someone to be an adult, and that is no small feat. Your preteen is trying to make the transition from being seen as a kid to being grown. Here are a few tips on how this book can best support you and your child.

## Try to Let Your Preteen Take Control

I'm not saying this will be easy, but it will be worth it. Allowing them to enjoy some control encourages them to get started, so they can see the possibilities and dream about what they want to do and who they want to be. They may mess up or overextend their "control" in the process, which is to be expected and presents a wonderful opportunity for you to help them identify their boundaries as they grow up and take on more responsibilities.

## Be Flexible

You work hard to schedule doctor appointments, take them to school and athletic activities, give them fulfilling life experiences, and more. When you have something planned, make sure they know. Maintain a calendar they can look at or just tell them in advance. You probably feel some comfort in knowing what to expect during your day, and they will as well. You have the final say when it comes to rules, but this book is here to help your child take charge of their day when they can, so they can learn how to make plans. But keep in mind that they are learning about flexibility and the critical lesson that all kinds of things will come up and change their plans.

## Weekends & Summer

For preteens who attend school, this edition focuses on making schedules for weekends and summer vacation (or "holiday" for our friends in the United Kingdom, Australia and some other English-speaking countries). Keep your eyes peeled for the companion Weekdays & After-School edition!

# A NOTE TO THE PRETEENS

You want to be your own boss, take control of your life, and make your own schedule? I get it. This book is exactly what you need to help you get started down that path because it will help you plan what you want to do with your time.

## Sometimes We Have To Do Boring Stuff

There are always things that we don't like to do, but they have to get done anyway. Maybe those things are boring or take a lot of work. Can you think of a few? Having a schedule will help you do more of what you want, but it does not mean you will not have to do the boring things anymore. It just means that you have the chance to build your schedule so you can do something you actually enjoy after you've had to scoop up the dog poop in the backyard (or completed another not-so-fun task).

## Always Be Flexible

The adults in your life work hard to schedule doctor appointments, take you to school and athletic activities, give you awesome life experiences, and more. When they have something planned, make sure you are ready to work it into your schedule and go with the flow. Adults have the final say when it comes to rules, but this book is here to help you take charge of your day when you have the chance, so you can learn how to make plans. But when you are an adult, you'll learn that all kinds of things will come up and change your plans, so be ready for this and just know that your schedule is here for when you don't have something else to do.

## Weekends & Summer

For preteens who attend school, this edition focuses on making schedules for weekends and summer vacation (or "holiday" for our friends in the United Kingdom, Australia and some other English-speaking countries). Keep your eyes peeled for the companion Weekdays & After-School edition!

# What You'll Need

A marker or
dark pen

A clock

& Your brain

# CONTENTS

GETTING STARTED

# GETTING STARTED

D o you like to read? Are you more of an artist? Perhaps you're a gamer. Or maybe you are an awesome skateboarder...

This is your chance. Create the perfect schedule, because you're awesome and making a schedule for your favorite things lets you spend more time being awesome.

To get started, what time do you usually wake up in the morning? (If you don't know, ask an adult in your house.) Write your normal wake-up time on the first line of your schedule.

**TIP:**
If another person in your family is making a schedule too, you don't have to have the same schedule! But if you want to do something together, look through the sections in this book and figure out what you want to do together. When you get your final schedule done at the end of this book, make sure you and the other person have the same time scheduled for whatever you chose to do together.

## MY SCHEDULE

### WAKE UP & EAT

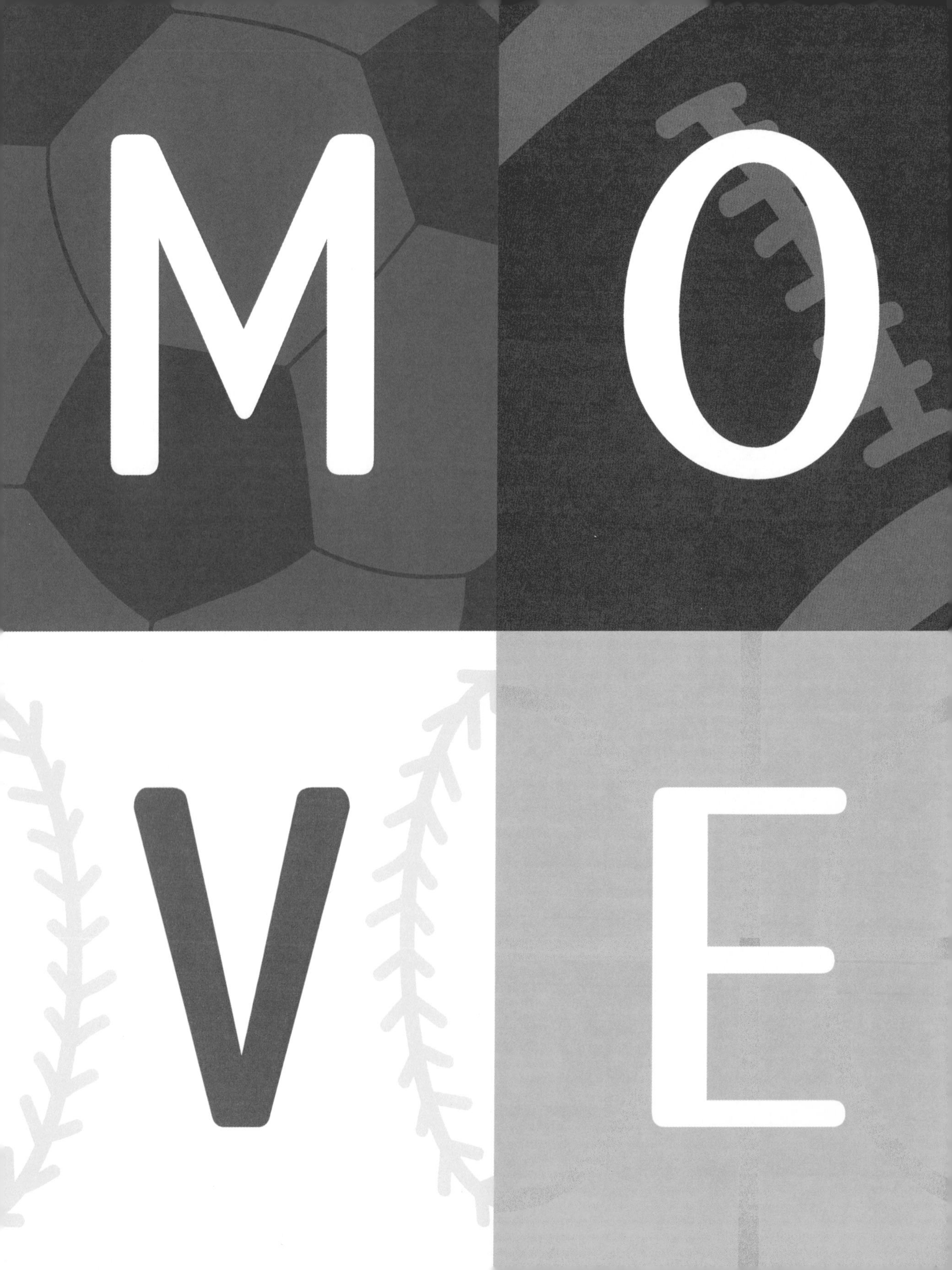
M O
V E

# MOVE

How much time do you think you should be active and exercise in a day?

Do you...

>    ... love riding your bike, roller-skating or skateboarding?

>    ... like dancing in your room while listening to music?

>    ... play basketball, football, baseball, or softball?

>    ... enjoy a walk with your dog or family?

>    ... have mad archery skills?

Maybe you do physical therapy or exercises from a doctor?

Are you the best swimmer in your family?

Do you have a trampoline to jump on?

Maybe you are the fastest runner in your class?

Getting up and moving is one of the best parts of being a human, and it keeps us ready for anything fun and exciting in life.

Use the next page to come up with more ideas for how to MOVE!

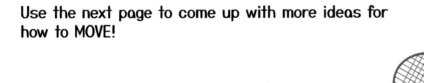

# Your MOVE Ideas

- Swimming.

- _____

- _____

- _____

- _____

- _____

- _____

- _____

- _____

- _____

- _____

- _____

- _____

- _____

- _____

- _____

It's true.
Some kids don't like to MOVE as much as other kids. If you feel sluggish or just enjoy laying around, try this trick:

Think about your favorite healthy snack. Now tell yourself: If I ride my bike or play with the dog for 30 minutes, then I'll ask for my favorite snack.

Then make sure you do something you enjoy after that, like TECH TIME or CHILL.

# MOVE

Now that you have tons of ideas in mind, let's add MOVE to your schedule.

Remember, the first line was for the time you wake up and eat a healthy breakfast. Our example says 6:30, but your line should reflect your actual schedule.

That means the next line is for MOVE. Again, we've got 7:00 in our example, but the time you put on your line is up to you!

| 6:30 | WAKE UP & EAT |
| 7:00 | MOVE |

## MY SCHEDULE

**TIP:**
Be realistic about your timing. If you think you need about 30 minutes to wake up and eat, then add 30 minutes to the first line's time, and that's what time you will start MOVE. If you need more or less time, that's fine too!

"
IF YOU DON'T LIKE
SOMETHING, CHANGE IT.
IF YOU CAN'T CHANGE IT,
CHANGE YOUR ATTITUDE. "

- MAYA ANGELOU

GROW

# GROW

GROW is for growing your brain. Your body grows all by itself, but your brain doesn't grow unless you help it along. This is your chance to decide what you want to learn.

How much time would you like to spend growing your brain? You could learn anything!

Do you want to know...

    ...how to speak another language?

    ...how to ride a bike?

    ...how to make a grilled cheese sandwich?

    ...how to jump rope?

    ...how to host a YouTube channel?

**TIP:**
Do you have school work to do? Whether it's math or reading, science or social studies, you can always do your homework during GROW time!

There are so many things you could learn!
You could also learn sign language or how to make a French braid.
Maybe you'd like to start a garden or get into Tae Kwon Do.

Use the next page to come up with more ideas for how to GROW!

### Did You Know?

For most people, it takes one to four years to learn another language, but you can only learn it one day at a time.

If you want to become bilingual or trilingual, just remember that you should be learning a little bit at a time, every day. That is how your brain learns best!

# Your GROW Ideas

- Learn to ride a bike.

Having a hard time coming up with what you want to learn?

Talk to people who know you, like an adult in your home. They may be able to get you started on a list of things you like but could learn more about.

# GROW

Y ou know what you want to learn, so let's add GROW to your schedule.

You already know your times for waking up and eating, then getting active with MOVE. So where can we put GROW? You got it! Slot GROW as the hour after MOVE!

Remember, your times can be different than our example times. This schedule is yours!

| 6:30 | WAKE UP & EAT |
| 7:00 | MOVE |
| 8:00 | GROW |

## MY SCHEDULE

CREATE

# CREATE

How much time would you like to spend creating something new? The human brain is great at creating. That's why we have so many ideas!

Do you...

   ...paint?

   ...draw?

   ...work with clay or Play-Doh?

   ...write stories or poems?

   ...scrapbook?

Building with LEGOs is a fun way to be creative. Maybe you enjoy helping the adults in your life when they're cooking or baking.

Have you ever created something new or developed an invention? YouTube has all kinds of videos that can help you learn how to create new things. Decide what you want to learn and ask an adult for permission to find a good video to teach you.

You could even make gifts for people you care about or for people you haven't seen in a long time.

Have you ever heard of a bullet journal? Ask your adult to look up "bullet journaling" with you and make your own planner!

Use the next page to come up with more ideas for how to CREATE!

17

# Your CREATE Ideas

- Draw my pets.

- 

- 

- 

- 

- 

- 

- 

- 

- 

- 

- 

- 

- 

- 

- 

What have you done in the last week that you are proud of?

Do you have any coloring books you like?

Sometimes I will find a picture I like and then try to draw it myself!

# CREATE

You are going to make some AMAZING stuff, so let's add CREATE to your schedule.

Fill in your first three lines below, like you did on previous pages. (If you forgot any of your times, you can go back and check!)

Now, fill in your time for CREATE as the hour after GROW.

## MY SCHEDULE

| 6:30 | WAKE UP & EAT |
| 7:00 | MOVE |
| 8:00 | GROW |
| 9:00 | CREATE |

# MEALS

# MEALS

Are you hungry? I'm starving!
We've done so much work, so let's add some time to eat!

Check with the adults in your life:

Do you usually have a snack in the morning or afternoon?

What time is lunch and how long does it take?

What about dinner? When is that and how much time should we schedule for it?

Use the next page to write down all these answers for MEALS!

I also added some of my favorite snacks below, because food is my favorite thing. Add some of yours too!

### FAVORITE FOODS!
- Chocolate
- Pretzels
- Berries
- Pears

# Your MEALS Answers

- Pretzels.

- 

- 

- 

- 

- 

- 

- 

-

# MEALS

I am totally ready to eat now, so let's add MEALS to your schedule. Fill in your first four times below, like you did on previous pages.

Then, add more times throughout the day, all the way down the list. As you do so, schedule your times for lunch and dinner, along with mid-morning and/or afternoon snacks.

## MY SCHEDULE

| | |
|---|---|
| _____ | _____ |
| _____ | _____ |
| _____ | _____ |
| _____ | _____ |
| _____ | _____ |
| _____ | _____ |
| _____ | _____ |
| _____ | _____ |
| _____ | _____ |
| _____ | _____ |
| _____ | _____ |
| _____ | _____ |
| _____ | _____ |
| _____ | _____ |
| _____ | _____ |
| _____ | _____ |
| _____ | _____ |

|  |  |
|---|---|
| 6:30 | WAKE UP & EAT |
| 7:00 | MOVE |
| 8:00 | GROW |
| 9:00 | CREATE |
| 10:00 | SNACK |
| 10:15 | |
| 11:15 | |
| 12:15 | LUNCH |
| 1:00 | |
| 2:00 | |
| 3:00 | SNACK |
| 3:15 | |
| 4:15 | |
| 5:15 | |
| 6:00 | DINNER |
| 7:00 | |
| 8:00 | |
| 9:00 | |

**TIP:**
You probably don't need an hour to eat a snack or lunch. Give yourself 15 minutes for a snack and 30 or 45 minutes for lunch. For dinner with your family, you'll probably want to schedule a full hour.

# CHILL

> " YOU ARE NO BETTER THAN
> ANYONE ELSE, AND NO ONE
> ELSE IS BETTER THAN YOU. "
>
> – KATHERINE JOHNSON

# CHILL

Do you ever just...relax?
Sometimes, simply sitting still for a few minutes and being alone is the best way to relax.

Have you ever...

      ...sat outside and listened to the birds chirp?

      ...watched the clouds drift through the sky?

      ...counted your breaths?

      ...walked barefoot in the grass?

      ...counted stars or looked for constellations at night?

Many people like to write in a journal or read a good book. Others might spend time meditating, maybe with the help of a YouTube video. Some just really like a nice refreshing nap.

Use the next page to write down all of your ideas for CHILL!

# Your CHILL Ideas

- Sit outside.

# CHILL

A re you pretty relaxed now? If so, let's add CHILL to your schedule.

Fill in your times and activities below, like you did on previous pages.

Now, let's slot CHILL on the next open line.

|  |  |
|------|----------|
| 6:30 | WAKE UP & EAT |
| 7:00 | MOVE |
| 8:00 | GROW |
| 9:00 | CREATE |
| 10:00 | SNACK |
| 10:15 | CHILL |
| 11:15 | |
| 12:15 | LUNCH |
| 1:00 | |
| 2:00 | |
| 3:00 | SNACK |
| 3:15 | |
| 4:15 | |
| 5:15 | |
| 6:00 | DINNER |
| 7:00 | |
| 8:00 | |
| 9:00 | |

## MY SCHEDULE

CONTRIBUTE

# CONTRIBUTE

## At Home

As you get older, it's important that you take some responsibility and help around the house. This is the easiest way to show those around you that you are getting older and more mature.

Do you...

>...wash the dishes?

>...help with the laundry?

>...clean your room?

>...take out the trash?

>...make small meals and snacks?

Do your family members ask you to help? What do they ask you to do? If you do not know how to do something, you can ask an adult to show you how. Or you can ask to watch a YouTube video about how to do it.

Does an adult in your life have a time of day when they are trying to do a lot of stuff? If you have a younger brother or sister, you could read a book to them or do a puzzle together during that time to help an adult have one less thing to worry about.

One of the best ways to show that you are older now is to CONTRIBUTE to the home by cleaning, helping, and spending time with people in your family.

How much time can you give to others during your day? It feels great when you can help make someone else's day a little bit better, so try to set aside 30 or 45 minutes each day.

## In Your Community

You can also contribute to your community in lots of ways. . .

- Mow a neighbor's yard
- Walk a neighbor's dog
- Volunteer to walk or play with animals at your local animal shelter
- Make a no-sew blanket for kids who are sick
- Write letters to people you love
- Make bathroom kits for local shelters (toothbrush, toothpaste, soap, deodorant)

Use the next page to write down all of your ideas for CONTRIBUTE!

# Your CONTRIBUTE Ideas

- <u>Mow neighbor's lawn.</u>
- _____
- _____
- _____
- _____
- _____
- _____
- _____
- _____
- _____

- _____
- _____
- _____
- _____
- _____
- _____
- _____
- _____

**TIP:**

If you play Hide & Seek with your little brother or sister, don't let them hide forever while you walk away. Not cool.

# CONTRIBUTE

Let's add CONTRIBUTE to your schedule.
Fill in your times and activities below, like you did on previous pages.

Instead of putting CONTRIBUTE on the next open line, I'm adding it to our example at 5:15. Many adults are making dinner around that time and could use some extra help with the little ones or with making dinner.

When could your CONTRIBUTE time best be used to help someone else?

|  |  |
|------|----------|
| 6:30 | WAKE UP & EAT |
| 7:00 | MOVE |
| 8:00 | GROW |
| 9:00 | CREATE |
| 10:00 | SNACK |
| 10:15 | CHILL |
| 11:15 | |
| 12:15 | LUNCH |
| 1:00 | |
| 2:00 | |
| 3:00 | SNACK |
| 3:15 | |
| 4:15 | |
| 5:15 | CONTRIBUTE |
| 6:00 | DINNER |
| 7:00 | |
| 8:00 | |
| 9:00 | |

## MY SCHEDULE

# TECH TIME

# TECH TIME

From television and video game systems to computers and smartphones, you probably have quite a few electronic devices in your home. Scheduling some TECH TIME will allow you to squeeze in some quality time with your favorite technology.

Do you...

> ...like to watch a certain show on TV?

> ...text your friends?

> ...watch an awesome YouTuber?

> ...have a favorite video game?

Use the next page to write down all your favorite things about TECH TIME!

## TIP FOR TALKING TO ADULTS:

Using electronics is not unhealthy IF you do it responsibly and in moderation. The adults in your life will be more likely to let you be on your favorite devices if you have a balanced schedule with time also dedicated to other important categories.

# Your TECH TIME Favorites

- Play video games.

# TECH TIME

Fill in your times and activities below, like you did on previous pages. Then, find a good slot for TECH TIME in your schedule.

Do you like to play games with a friend at the same time? Make sure you let them know when you want to play and that you have other things to do afterward, so they know when you are going to need to finish up.

My favorite time for tech is 3:15, after I've had an afternoon snack.

|  |  |
|------|----------|
| 6:30 | WAKE UP & EAT |
| 7:00 | MOVE |
| 8:00 | GROW |
| 9:00 | CREATE |
| 10:00 | SNACK |
| 10:15 | CHILL |
| 11:15 | |
| 12:15 | LUNCH |
| 1:00 | |
| 2:00 | |
| 3:00 | SNACK |
| 3:15 | TECH TIME |
| 4:15 | |
| 5:15 | CONTRIBUTE |
| 6:00 | DINNER |
| 7:00 | |
| 8:00 | |
| 9:00 | |

## MY SCHEDULE

# HANG OUT

# HANG OUT

"The more, the merrier!" People say that because sometimes life is more fun when you're hanging out with friends or family. What are your favorite things to do with other people?

Do you...

> ...go somewhere with friends?

> ...play card games or board games, or do puzzles?

> ...get everyone in your home together for movie nights?

> ...cook together?

> ...have friends over for a soccer game or playing cornhole in the backyard?

Use the next page to write down all of your favorite things to do when you HANG OUT.

# Your HANG OUT Favorites

- Movie night.

**TIP:**

Open a board game or puzzle to hang out with younger kids and still have fun! Challenge younger kids to solve a puzzle fast by timing them, or ask everyone to compete in a board game together. If a child does not know how to read for board games, try playing matching games with a deck of cards.

# HANG OUT

Fill in your times and activities below, like you did on previous pages. Then, find a good space for HANG OUT on your schedule.

My time is 7:00, right after dinner. Everyone is already together after eating, so we pick something fun to do then.

If you want, ask everyone to vote on something to do tonight!

## MY SCHEDULE

|  |  |
|------|----------|
| 6:30 | WAKE UP & EAT |
| 7:00 | MOVE |
| 8:00 | GROW |
| 9:00 | CREATE |
| 10:00 | SNACK |
| 10:15 | CHILL |
| 11:15 | |
| 12:15 | LUNCH |
| 1:00 | |
| 2:00 | |
| 3:00 | SNACK |
| 3:15 | TECH TIME |
| 4:15 | |
| 5:15 | CONTRIBUTE |
| 6:00 | DINNER |
| 7:00 | HANG OUT |
| 8:00 | |
| 9:00 | |

# FINALLY...

# FINALLY...

You're almost there! You should still have some spaces open in your schedule. How do we finish filling it in?
Go back through each section of this book and figure out
which sections are your favorites. Then, come back to your
schedule and write in an extra slot for those! Here are mine...

TECH TIME - I will put it at 4:15
so I can play a little more in the afternoon.

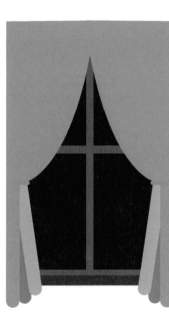

CREATE - I will slot it at 1:00
to make something cool after lunch.
So that leaves 11:15 and 2:00 open during the day...

I will add another hour of CHILL at 11:15
to read some of the books I found at the library.

I want one more hour of MOVE at 2:00
so I can go outside and ride my bike.
Hopefully the weather is nice!
But there are still openings after HANG OUT...

I will fill one more space with HANG OUT, then finish
the day with BED! (If you have a time you must
be in bed, make sure you include that on your schedule!)

When you're done, hand your schedule over to an adult in your home so
they can see your masterpiece!

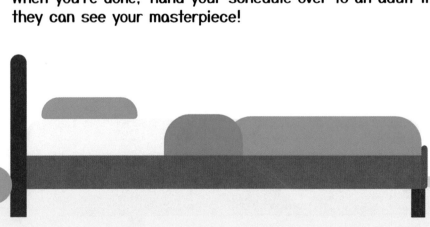

# FINALLY. . .

| | |
|---|---|
| 6:30 | WAKE UP & EAT |
| 7:00 | MOVE |
| 8:00 | GROW |
| 9:00 | CREATE |
| 10:00 | SNACK |
| 10:15 | CHILL |
| 11:15 | CHILL |
| 12:15 | LUNCH |
| 1:00 | CREATE |
| 2:00 | MOVE |
| 3:00 | SNACK |
| 3:15 | TECH TIME |
| 4:15 | TECH TIME |
| 5:15 | CONTRIBUTE |
| 6:00 | DINNER |
| 7:00 | HANG OUT |
| 8:00 | HANG OUT |
| 9:00 | BED |

## MY SCHEDULE

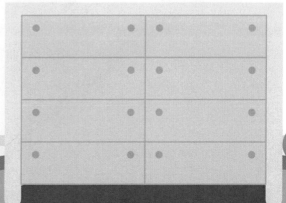

# EXTRA WORKSHEETS

# EXTRA WORKSHEETS

## Making Changes to Your Schedule

If your new schedule doesn't work for you today, make a new one! You can move things around to make it better.

One summer, my kids changed their schedules every week! They moved time for CONTRIBUTE to read a book to their sister, and they decided that riding their bike in the morning made them feel better the rest of the day.

## Different Schedules for Different Days of the Week

Does your schedule change through the week?

Maybe you split your time between two different homes. Maybe you have practice every Wednesday and Saturday. Use the Extra Worksheets to make different schedules for different days!

When you run out of pages in this book, just grab a blank piece of paper and make a new schedule!

# EXTRA WORKSHEETS

What will you name your schedule?

# EXTRA WORKSHEETS

# EXTRA WORKSHEETS

# EXTRA WORKSHEETS

# EXTRA WORKSHEETS

# EXTRA WORKSHEETS

# EXTRA WORKSHEETS

# APPENDIX: LIFE SKILLS

**Did You Know?**
When you work your way through this book, you
are developing these life skills:

Growth Mindset

Self-Control

Planning

Self-Leadership

Confidence

Organizing

Decision-Making

Balance

Self-Care

Made in United States
Orlando, FL
11 June 2023

34009254R10031